THE ALABASTER MEN
SACRED IMAGES FROM MEDIEVAL ENGLAND

DANIEL KATZ LTD

THE ALABASTER MEN
SACRED IMAGES FROM MEDIEVAL ENGLAND

CATALOGUE BY

FRANCIS CHEETHAM OBE

IMAGES OF MEDIEVAL ENGLAND
THE ICONOGRAPHY OF ALABASTER CARVINGS

FRANCIS CHEETHAM

The Golden Legend was compiled about 1260 by Jacobus de Voragine who later, in 1292, became archbishop of Genoa. The diverse sources of his book range from the 2nd century to the 13th century and are primarily stories of saints and an expansion of the often sparse details in the Gospels of the lives of Christ and his mother.

Many of the stories of saints are amazing, and to the modern reader, quite unbelievable. Indeed since the Council of Trent in the 16th century, the Church has dealt severely with these fantastic stories. But the *Golden Legend* was eagerly read in the Middle Ages and its popularity is attested by the fact that some one thousand[1] manuscripts have survived. After the Bible it was the most widely read book.

With the invention of printing in the 1450s, the book was readily available, both in the original Latin and in the developing vernacular languages of Western Europe. William Caxton "Englished" the *Golden Legend* and printed it in 1483. Artists and craftsmen, including the alabaster carvers of England were influenced in their work by the *Legend.* Many scenes and details in painting or sculpture can be related directly to the *Golden Legend.* This is not to say that the Nottingham alabaster sculptors for example, read the book before carving a panel. The influence of the book was much more subtle as it pervaded the whole of medieval society. For example, it would have provided vivid and picturesque stories for preachers to use, so that illiteracy was not a bar to familiarity with the fantastic lives of many of the saints, of whom, in many cases very little was known historically; the lack of information being made up over the centuries by the imagination of story-tellers and writers. It is concerning the lives of the saints that the *Legend* is most colourful, especially those who lived after the writing of the Gospels. St Lawrence and his martyrdom is an example – a panel of this scene is in the present exhibition. A quotation from the *Golden Legend* sets the scene – "Decius (the Emperor) said to Lawrence: 'Either you will sacrifice to the gods, or you will spend the night being tortured!' Lawrence: 'My night has no darkness, and all things gleam in the light!' Decius gave his orders: 'Let an iron bed be brought, and let this stubborn Lawrence rest on it !' The executioners therefore stripped him, laid him out on the iron grill, piled burning coals under it, and pressed heated iron pitchforks upon his body."[2].

St John the Evangelist too is in the exhibition. The palm he holds is a detail taken from the *Golden Legend.* The Virgin on her deathbed said to John "Therefore you, John, must have someone carry this palm branch in front of the litter when you convey my body to the sepulchre", and later Peter said to John "You should be the one to carry it (the palm), since you, a virgin, were chosen by the Lord, and it is fitting that a virgin should carry the Virgin's palm."[3].

Many of the saints whose lives are described in the *Legend* do not find their way into the repertoire of the alabaster men; perhaps surprisingly there are no images of St Francis of Assisi. Two saints in the present exhibition are included in the Legend, but two are not: St Catherine of Alexandra and, as we have seen, St Lawrence are in the Legend, but neither St Dorothy nor St Erasmus are mentioned. There were clearly other sources in addition to the *Golden Legend* and it should be borne in mind that when Caxton translated the *Legend* into English and printed it, he omitted some saints, but added some sixty more[4]. The texts circulating in the Middle Ages were certainly not immutable.

There was a desire in medieval times to fill out the bare facts of the Gospels, especially those concerning the Virgin Mary, and the *Golden Legend* filled that need. The development of the cult of the Virgin promoted speculation about almost every event in her life, including her conception.

The Meeting at the Golden Gate, alabaster, England, 15th century. Bought from Christie's on 21 May 1987.

The Dedication of The Virgin, alabaster, England, 15th century. Museo Arqueológico Nacional, Madrid, Spain.

The *Golden Legend* relates[5] how Joachim married to Anna for twenty years without offspring, went to the Temple in Jerusalem to make an offering. He was angrily ordered away for his childless state, which clearly showed that he was not blessed by the Lord. Joachim was ashamed to go home and instead went and lived with his shepherds. Then one day an angel appeared and announced that his prayers had been heard and that his wife would bear him a daughter and she should be called Mary. The angel continued that Anna would be waiting for him at the Golden Gate of Jerusalem. Meanwhile, Anna was weeping bitterly not knowing where her husband had gone, when the same angel appeared to her and revealed that she too should go to the Golden Gate where she would meet her husband as he returned. So they met as the angel had predicted and went home awaiting the fulfilment of the divine promise. Anna conceived and brought forth a daughter, and they called her Mary. Although English alabaster panels illustrating these events are not common, an attractive panel was sold at Christie's on 21 May 1987, showing both the angel appearing to Joachim and the famous kiss at the Golden Gate, by which Mary was conceived immaculately.

The birth of Mary, which is also carved on a number of panels, is followed in the *Golden Legend* with a description of how Mary at the age of three was taken to the Temple with offerings. Around the Temple there were fifteen steps, corresponding to the fifteen gradual Psalms. The child was set down at the lowest step and walked unaided up the steps as if she were already fully grown[6].

An English alabaster panel in the Museo Arqueológico Nacional in Madrid, shows this scene with the proud parents looking on.

Many other details inspired by the *Golden Legend* are to be seen in the alabaster carvings. In the 14ᵗʰ century horizontal panels of the Adoration of the Magi, there is a mysterious female. In a panel which is in the Long Melford Church, Suffolk, she adjusts the cushion behind Mary's back. This female is one of the two midwives mentioned in the Legend. The Magi, as in the 15ᵗʰ century panel in the present exhibition, are three in number and are kings (but there are no midwives). The Legend gives them the names of Caspar, Balthasar and Melchior[7], and concludes this description by mentioning that after their deaths, the bodies of the Magi were taken to Constantinople and later transferred to Milan. "When the Emperor Henry took possession of Milan, he moved the bodies to Cologne on the Rhine river."[8]. The shrine of the Three Kings is still in Cologne Cathedral.

As for the midwives, the *Golden Legend*[9] states: "... when the hour had come for Mary to be delivered, Joseph called two midwives, the one being Zebel and the other Salome. When Zebel, probing and realising that Mary was a virgin cried out that a virgin had given birth, Salome did not believe it and tried to find out for herself, but her hand instantly withered; then an angel appeared and told her to touch the child, and she was cured immediately." Presumably on the Long Melford panel, the one midwife shown is Zebel, the believing midwife. In the 15ᵗʰ century, panels showing the Adoration of Mary and Joseph sometimes include both Zebel and Salome. Such a panel is to be seen in the V&A Museum[10]. The incident of Salome's withered hand was a salutary reminder of the truth of the Virginity of Mary. Nevertheless by the second half of the 15ᵗʰ century, the two midwives are seen no longer in alabaster. Being based on legend, their appearance was presumably eventually discouraged by the church.

The ox and the ass are included, but mention of them in the *Golden Legend*[11] ultimately derives from the prophesy of Isaiah[12]. "The ox knoweth his owner, and the ass his master's crib."

Medieval art was didactic. It was there to express in paint or stone the Gospel stories, to encourage believers to admire the heroic lives of the saints and also occasionally to make a doctrinal point. For example, the *Golden Legend*[13] describes what happened after St Thomas – doubting Thomas – refused to believe in the Assumption of the Virgin. "Then suddenly the girdle that had encircled her body fell intact into his hands, and he realised that the Blessed Virgin had really been assumed body and soul." This detail of St Thomas holding, or catching, the belt from Mary's gown, is to be seen on many of the English alabaster Assumption panels, including the one in this exhibition. The falling girdle confirmed the truth of the Assumption.

The Passion of Christ, altarpiece, alabaster, England, 15th century. Nottingham Castle Museum.

While the *Golden Legend* clearly influenced the art of the Middle Ages, the fundamental basis was, of course, the Gospels themselves. Most of the panels illustrate scenes described in the New Testament. To take the altarpieces of the Passion of Christ for example, such as we see in Nottingham Castle Museum, panels of the Betrayal, the Flagellation, the Entombment and the Resurrection (all to be seen in the present exhibition), are all faithful descriptions of the Gospel scenes, but transmuted so that we are looking at panels peopled with medieval soldiers, medieval ruffians and medieval angels.

Panels of the Life of the Virgin, such as the Swansea altarpiece in the V&A Museum, are likewise descriptions straight from the Gospels. They are the Annunciation and the Adoration of the Magi (both in the exhibition) and the Ascension, although admittedly with some Golden Legend details. Only the Assumption (also in this exhibition), although hallowed by ancient tradition, is not described in the Gospels.

Some of the detailed imagery in the carvings is also inspired by the written symbolism of the New Testament. God the Holy Spirit is described in St Mark's Gospel[14] as a dove, a symbol almost universally used to this day, and to be seen

The Swansea Altarpiece, alabaster, England, 1450-1500. Victoria and Albert Museum, London.

Saint Michael weighing souls with the Virgin Interceding, alabaster, England, 15th century. Victoria and Albert Museum, London.

on most of the Trinity panels. In the Agony in the Garden panel in this exhibition, Christ is shown praying and facing a chalice. This is a direct reference to the Gospel symbolism, "... if it be possible, let this cup pass from me..."[15]. However, the symbolic cup has been imaginatively developed by showing it as a chalice surmounted by the wafer, symbolic of the sacrifice of Christ in the Mass. Old Testament scenes and imagery are rare in the extreme. Even the Romanesque images of the souls in the Bosom of Abraham have been transposed into the souls of the blessed, held in a napkin, by God the Father in the Trinity panels.

THE MEDIEVAL THEATRE

Much has been written, especially by Dr Hildburgh[16], about the influence of the medieval theatre on the design of the alabaster carvings, but also more tentatively by Professor Prior writing earlier in 1913[17]. However, one should be cautious about the direct influence of the stage on the alabasters. One should certainly question the notion that the alabastermen seeing a play would then go back to their workshops and incorporate actual details of the play in their carvings. It is more fruitful to appreciate that the craftsmen were open to all kinds of influence than to become too concerned about which medium influenced the other. The craftsmen were working in a distinct cultural environment which expressed its ideas in wall paintings, stained glass, sculpture, drama, manuscripts and by the 15th century, in woodcuts and other prints.

If the theatre did influence the alabaster designs, this influence may ultimately be traced back to *The Golden Legend* and other stories. As W G Ryan states in his introduction to the *Golden Legend*[18]. "Students of the late medieval mystery plays and miracle plays will see that many of these plays may well have drawn upon the Legend for setting, characters, action, dialogue, and 'business.'" He gives as an example the account of Christ's visit to hell in the chapter on the Resurrection.

However, having said that, the blackening of the faces of villains and executioners, as we see in the panel of the Flagellation in this exhibition, may be a direct stage influence. Likewise, the identification of an exceptionally evil person by headgear from which a small dragon projects may also be attributed to the medieval theatre. This may be seen, for example, in the panel of the Martyrdom of St Catherine in the collection of the Society of Antiquaries, where a dragon emerges from the crown of the Emperor. In addition, images showing St Michael in scaly legs may be interpreted as the feathered tights worn by the actor playing the role of the archangel. An example is in the V&A Museum[19]. Hildburgh's theories about the influence of the theatre on the design of the Resurrection panels, such as the one in this exhibition, with Christ stepping onto a sleeping soldier, the deep side of the tomb and the use of the cross staff, are more questionable, but undoubtedly ingenious.

PRINTS

Whatever the possible influences on the design of the alabaster carvings, one thing is certain. The basic designs were not the creation of the alabaster men. However, no two carvings are exactly the same, so there was always room for

Christk Before Pilate, woodcut, Antwerp, 1500.
Bibliothèque Royal, Brussels.

some individual expression. Designs can be closely paralleled on the Continent and in other media in England. In particular, certainly by the middle of the 15th century, Continental woodcuts, mainly from the Netherlands, Germany and France, had a demonstrable influence on the alabaster designs. A remarkable direct influence may be seen in a woodcut produced in Antwerp in 1500 of Christ before Pilate[20] on an alabaster panel in the V&A Museum of Christ before Herod[21]. The similarity of the legs of the figures and the hems of their garments is striking. A French woodcut of the Betrayal of 1450 is similar in design to the alabaster panels of the same subject[22]. A Swabian print of 1450-1460[23] of the Agony in the Garden is reminiscent in design of a panel in the V&A Museum[24]. It has a chalice representing the cup, similar to the panel in this exhibition and to the panel in the V&A Museum. However, it has no wafer above the chalice.

PAINTING

Many of the alabaster carvings have lost much of their colour, but it is unusual for there to be no trace at all of the original paint in the recesses of the carvings. The colouring of the carvings was clearly an integral part of the whole operation – this applied to tomb effigies as well as the smaller panels and images. Paint was often applied without a ground, for the alabaster itself provided a smooth and non-absorbent surface.

The lower part of the panels was usually painted green which was decorated with 'daisies' consisting of white dots enclosing one red dot. The upper background was often gilded, with the surface usually decorated with applied dots of gesso which were also gilded. If the gesso blobs have become detached with age, a sprinkling of white dots in the gilding may be seen, as is evident in the Trinity and Crucifixion panels in this exhibition. Usually the details of the eyes of individuals were painted in, the carver leaving simply the ball of the eye to be so decorated.

Although painting was an important part of the image, panel, or tomb, it was unusual for the craftsmen to paint over all the surface. Almost always, areas of the alabaster itself were left to contrast with the painted features. The colours commonly used were green, red, brown and black with some gilding.

ORIGIN AND DEVELOPMENT OF THE CARVINGS

The exploitation of the alabaster stone suitable for carving which, judging from contemporary records was situated mainly in South Derbyshire and the adjoining corner of Staffordshire, was developed initially by the carvers of tombs. The continuous history of the industry is now thought to start with the effigy of Edward II in Gloucester Cathedral, which dates from c 1330[25]. The earliest written reference to alabaster images appears to be from 1341 to 1347. A notable early reference is dated 1382 and refers to alabaster images exported by Cosmato Gentilis, Pope Urban VI's representative in England. Two images of Saints Peter and Paul, now in the church of Santa Croce in Gerusalemme in Rome, are possibly carvings surviving from this exportation by Gentilis. The 14th century Flawford figures of the Virgin and Child, St Peter and an

Christ before Herod, alabaster, England, early 16th century.
Victoria and Albert Museum, London.

unidentified bishop (probably St Thomas Becket), now in Nottingham Castle Museum, appear to be of about the same date – 1380. Also a little earlier than this date, are a number of horizontal panels of the Adoration of the Magi.

By the very end of the 14th century the alabastermen started to produce vertical panels measuring approximately 40 cms x 25 cms and designed to be arranged as a series, in the shape of altarpieces. The panels were secured to the wooden framework by wires which were held by lead plugs in the back of the carvings. Nottingham appears to have emerged as the main centre for the panels and images, for although there are documentary references of alabastermen working in a number of other places, notably Burton on Trent and York, the records for Nottingham are more numerous and cover a longer period of time.

The altarpieces mainly illustrated the Life of the Virgin and the Passion of Christ, these being the two themes which dominated the work of the alabaster carvers throughout the 15th century until the Reformation in the 16th century. Certainly panels were also made to be shown individually in wooden housings, or in the case of St John's Heads, sometimes veiled with a cloth. Such single panels and images would be found in the homes of well-to-do people, as well as in churches. Perhaps the most remarkable of these individual panels were the Heads of St John the Baptist, many dating from the late 15th century, a fine example being included in this exhibition.

The recorded numbers of surviving alabaster carvings indicate how these two themes of Mary and Jesus surpassed all other themes. The largest number of surviving panels are of the following subjects: Annunciation about 100; Adoration of the Magi over 100; Assumption about 100; Coronation 120. These are all standard panels in the Virgin altarpieces. The theme of the Passion of Christ includes the following panels which have survived in the largest numbers: Betrayal over 100, Flagellation 74, Crucifixion 127, Entombment about 100, Resurrection 144. The other large group of panels/figures are the Trinities which often formed the central panel of an altarpiece; over 100 are recorded. Panels of the Ascension, which were sometimes included in the Virgin altarpieces, is the only other single subject of which there is a significant high number; 46 are recorded.

So successful were the English alabaster sculptors that they developed an important export trade. Their work is still to be found in churches and museums in countries in Western Europe, ranging from Iceland to Croatia. The greatest number are in France, the biggest concentration there being in Normandy. Whole altarpieces as well as over 2000 individual carvings survive, sometimes it seems in the churches that originally ordered them. Indeed an altarpiece of the Life of St James, which is dated by a document of 1456, is still in the Cathedral of Santiago de Compostela, in north west Spain. Since the great shrine of St James Major is in the Cathedral, the altarpiece must have been a special order, and indeed it was taken there by an English priest named John Goodyear[26].

THE REFORMATION

This remarkable English activity, with its international ramifications, came to a sad and final end as the result of a series of government decisions. The action of Henry VIII in suppressing the monasteries caused the loss of potential clients and also flooded the market with monastery furnishings (unless they were destroyed). However, it was during the reign of his son, Edward VI, that the alabaster carving industry suffered a body blow. In January 1550[27], the destruction of all images was decreed by the extreme Protestant government, including specifically images in alabaster. Suddenly there was no market for the carvings, and the alabastermen were out of a job. There is no evidence that the industry resumed after the premature death of Edward VI in 1553, when his successor, Mary, returned the country to Roman Catholicism, even though it is known that images were being made again for the denuded parish churches and cathedrals. Mary's premature death in 1558 restored Protestantism as the state religion when her sister Elizabeth came to the throne. This was definitely the end so far as the alabastermen were concerned, except of course, for the tomb carvers. The fashion for alabaster tombs continued and was not forbidden by law, since sepulchral effigies were not regarded as 'images'.

Shakespeare recognised this fashion in the *Merchant of Venice* when he placed the following words in Gratiano's mouth: "Why should a man whose blood is warm within, sit like his grandsire, cut in alabaster?"

NOTES

[1] W G RYAN, *The Golden Legend*, Princeton (1993), Vol I, p XIII.

[2] *The Golden Legend*, translated by W G RYAN, Princeton (1993), Vol II, pp 79-80.

[3] *The Golden Legend*, translated by W G RYAN, Princeton (1993), Vol II, pp 66-67.

[4] W G RYAN, *The Golden Legend*, Princeton (1993), Vol I, p XIV.

[5] *The Golden Legend*, translated by W G RYAN, Princeton (1993). Vol II, pp 151-152.

[6] *The Golden Legend*, translated by W G RYAN, Princeton (1993), Vol II, p 152.

[7] *The Golden Legend*, translated by W G RYAN, Princeton (1993), Vol I, p 79.

[8] *The Golden Legend*, translated by W G RYAN, Princeton (1993), Vol I, p 84.

[9] *The Golden Legend*, translated by W G RYAN, Princeton (1993), Vol I, p 38.

[10] F CHEETHAM, *English Medieval Alabasters*, Oxford (1984), p 179, cat 106, illus.

[11] *The Golden Legend*, translated by W G RYAN, Princeton (1993), Vol I, p 38.

[12] ISAIAH: 1:3

[13] *The Golden Legend*, translated by W G RYAN, Princeton (1993), Vol II, p 82.

[14] MARK I: 10

[15] MATTHEW: 26:39

[16] W L HILDBURGH, *Archaeologia* XCIII (1949), pp 51-101.

[17] *Society of Antiquaries Catalogue of English Medieval Alabaster Work* (1913), p 21.

[18] W G RYAN, *The Golden Legend*, Princeton (1993), Vol I, p XV.

[19] F CHEETHAM, *English Medieval Alabasters*, Oxford (1984), p 134, cat 63, illus.

[20] F CHEETHAM, *English Medieval Alabasters*, Oxford (1984), p 20, illus.

[21] F CHEETHAM, *English Medieval Alabasters*, Oxford (1984), p 232, cat 159, illus.

[22] F CHEETHAM, *English Medieval Alabasters*, Oxford (1984), p 20, illus.

[23] R S FIELD, *Fifteenth Century Woodcuts and Metalcuts*, National Gallery of Art, Washington (1965), no 33, illus.

[24] F CHEETHAM, *English Medieval Alabasters*, Oxford (1984), p 223, cat 150, illus.

[25] C BLAIR, *Journal of the Church Monuments Society*, Vol VII (1992), pp 3-18.

[26] W L HILDBURGH, *Antiquaries Journal VI*, (1926), pp 304-307.

[27] J R TANNER, *Tudor Constitutional Documents* 1485-1603, Cambridge (1951), p 113.

CATALOGUE

Saint Catherine of Alexandria, alabaster, England, 15th century. Tromsø Museum, Norway.

According to The Golden Legend[1] Catherine refused the offer of marriage by the Roman Emperor Maxentius, saying 'I have given myself as his bride to Christ..', and protested against the Emperor's persecution of Christians.

The saint stands with a sword in her right hand and a wheel (broken) in her left. The sword which has a belt curled round the scabbard in a decorative way – one can just make out the buckle of the belt – represents her martyrdom by beheading. St Catherine, however, is popularly associated with the wheel which represents the instrument of her torture. She was condemned to be killed by whirling spiked wheels, but the wheels broke and the torturers were killed by the flying broken pieces, after which she was executed by the sword.

St Catherine wears her hair loose, falling down over her shoulders as was the fashion among ladies in the 15th century. As the daughter of a king, the saint is usually shown wearing a crown, which is visible in this carving although it has been mostly chipped away.

Beneath the feet of the triumphant martyred saint lies the Emperor himself, a diminutive figure indicating his lack of importance in relation to the saint herself. He wears a low-belted tunic and as Emperor a crown, and is shown in the act of stabbing himself in the chest with a dagger, in remorse for his evil acts.

The intricately looped tasselled cord drawing together the top of St Catherine's cloak is similar to the fastening on the cloak of the Virgin in the Assumption panel in the present exhibition. This emphasises the widespread popularity of this 15th century feature among the rich and powerful, which is also to be seen on alabaster tombs of the period. Some are listed in the description of the Assumption panel, another is on a male figure, that of the Duke of Suffolk who died in 1491[2]. His effigy is in Wingfield church, Suffolk, and this cloak-fastening is similar, but not so long, as that of our St Catherine figure.

There is virtually no colour remaining on the carving.

St Catherine was a popular saint, with several pages devoted to her in *The Golden Legend.* No less than thirty three alabaster figures of her are recorded, including one in the V&A Museum[3], as well as a number of panels from her life which were made up into altarpieces. A complete St Catherine altarpiece which was formerly in the church of St Catherine in Venice, is now in the Ca' d'Oro. A standing figure of the saint is in the Tromsø Museum, Norway.

Alabaster
Second half of the 15th century

Measurements: 74 cm x 26 cm

NOTES

[1] *The Golden Legend,* translated by W G RYAN, Princeton (1993), Vol II, p 337.
[2] A GARDNER, *Alabaster Tombs,* Cambridge (1940), fig 275.
[3] F CHEETHAM, *English Medieval Alabasters,* Oxford (1984) p 84, cat 13, illus.

19

The Martyrdom of Saint Catherine, alabaster, England, 15th century. Society of Antiquaries, London.

The carving is similar to a number of panels showing the martyrdom of St Catherine, who is of course, most frequently associated with the 'Catherine Wheel' by which she was tortured. She was, however, eventually beheaded by the sword.

Two details indicate that the panel is of St Dorothy rather than St Catherine. The severed head with its long tresses of hair lying on the ground is encircled with what appears to be a fillet or garland of flowers, whereas St Catherine is almost always shown wearing a crown. Another significant detail is the figure on the left of the panel holding a basket of fruit and flowers, which is an attribute of St Dorothy. During the reign of the Emperor Diocletian, according to the legend of her life, a young lawyer called Theophilus taunted her on her way to execution for refusing to worship idols. He asked her to send him fruits from the garden of paradise after her death. Thereafter, an angel presented him with a basket containing three apples and three roses.

The alabaster carvers occasionally used a standard design of one saint and with some alterations used it for another saint. This seems to have happened to her. There are, for example, in the V&A Museum[1] and in the collection of the Society of Antiquaries, two St Catherine panels which are reminiscent of our panel. There would appear to be no other alabaster panel surviving of the martyrdom of St Dorothy, although there is a standing figure of the saint flanking the St Catherine altarpiece in the Ca' d'Oro, Venice.

As usual with the alabaster carvings, the assembled group is dressed in typical medieval garb, for it was only with the Renaissance and a growing awareness of the development of dress from ancient times that artists, first of all on the continent, attempted to show dress contemporary with the event.

A high official representing the Roman Emperor (he cannot be the Emperor himself for he wears no crown), stands at the centre of the panel. He wears a medieval hat, gown and belt, with a short cape or tippet over his shoulders. In his left hand he holds a staff, doubtless denoting his authority and power, looking at the bowl of fruit and flowers.

The executioner, in hat and belted tunic, replaces the sword in its sheath which he rests on the back of the headless saint. Around, the armed guards, all with hats, are looking on.

Very little of the original medieval colour has survived. The whole panel appears to have been painted over later with a brownish wash.

Alabaster
15th century

Measures: 43.5 cms x 31 cms

NOTES

[1] F CHEETHAM, *English Medieval Alabasters*, Oxford (1984), p 91, cat 20, illus.

21

The Martyrdom of Saint Erasmus, alabaster, England, 15th century. Society of Antiquaries, London.

The panel might well be described as the medieval equivalent of the modern horror video. Little is known historically of the life of St Erasmus, although he is believed to have died about AD 300. He became the patron saint of sailors and it is believed that the maritime windlass, chosen as his emblem, mistakenly became associated with his martyrdom.

He is shown lying on a trestle table, stripped of all his clothes except for a pair of short underpants and, rather incongruously, his bishop's mitre. His feet are bound with a rope which is being pulled with both hands by a torturer who kneels on his left leg beneath the trestle table. At his side another torturer prods the saint with a four pronged instrument. Two other torturers standing behind the table, wind the saint's entrails from his belly with a windlass. In spite of this horrific treatment, the saint maintains a serene expression, indicating his belief in a rich reward in heaven.

In the centre of the panel stands the crowned figure of the Roman Emperor with two more of his men, holding a sword in his left hand.

In a similar way in which the design of the Martyrdom of St Dorothy in this exhibition derived from the design of the St Catherine martyrdoms, panels of St Erasmus are of a similar design to the Martyrdoms of St Lawrence, who is shown lying on a gridiron instead of a trestle table. Thirteen panels of the martyrdom of St Erasmus are recorded, one example being in the collection of the Society of Antiquaries.

Some traces of paint survive, black on the beards of the men and on the Emperor's sword. At the bottom of the panel are the remains of the typical green ground decorated with daisy patterns.

Alabaster
15th century

Measures: 41 cms x 25.5 cms

St John The Evangelist, alabaster, England, 15th century.
Musée Curtius, Liège, Belgium.

Two characteristic features of images of St John the Evangelist are the palm which he carries in his left hand, and unlike the other apostles, except very occasionally St Philip, his lack of a beard.

In his right hand he has a holy book on which a cross is painted. A book is a common feature held by many saints, but with St John it is particularly appropriate, reminding us of his authorship of the Fourth Gospel. On some carvings instead of the book, he is shown holding a chalice from which emerges a small dragon or viper, referring to the legend[1] that he drank from a poisoned cup offered to him by the pagan high priest of Diana, without ill effect. An example is to be seen in the Musée Curtius, Liège, Belgium.

The palm is a feature of many saints, representing their martyrdom, but although according to tradition St John was persecuted under the Emperor Domitian, he ended his days peacefully at an advanced age at Ephesus. However, *The Golden Legend*[2] tells us that the palm was given to him by the Virgin which he carried before her funeral bier.

As usual with medieval English alabasters, the details of the eyes are not carved (except in this case the eyelids), but are meant to be painted on. Some colour survives on the figure, especially red on the cloak and green (now blackened) on the palm. On the saint's book is some red and the cross is in gold.

Figures of St John the Evangelist in alabaster survive in some quantity, no less than thirty four being recorded. This large number is because on many altarpieces, for example the Swansea altarpiece in the V&A Museum, St John commonly balances the flanking figure of St John the Baptist. Some panels of the life of St John survive which were inspired by *The Golden Legend*; his torture in boiling oil from which he emerged miraculously unscathed, and his assumption – this rare subject being in the Musée des Antiquités, Rouen.

The figure of St John must have been very familiar to the people of medieval England, since he was always represented in churches with the Virgin Mary on the wooden rood-screens separating the choir from the nave, before they were so ruthlessly destroyed at the Reformation.

Alabaster
15th century

Measures: 44 cms x 12 cms

NOTES

[1] *The Golden Legend,* translated by W G RYAN, Princeton (1993), Vol I, p 53.
[2] *The Golden Legend,* translated by W G RYAN, Princeton (1993), Vol II, p 79-80.

The Martyrdom of Saint Lawrence, alabaster, England, 1450-1500. Nottingham Castle Museum.

This finely carved panel shows St Lawrence being slowly killed by being roasted on a gridiron. The similarity in design, although not in the style of carving with the panel of St Erasmus in this exhibition is clear.

St Lawrence was a deacon of the church in Rome and was martyred about AD 258. One of Rome's most famous martyrs, there are five ancient basilicas in the city dedicated to him, including that built over his tomb at St Lawrence outside the Walls. In more recent times, Philip II's great 16th century building of the Escorial near Madrid was dedicated to St Lawrence.

The dramatic legend[1] of his martyrdom no doubt attracted the attention of artists and helped spread the cult. The English alabaster carvers of the 15th century were affected by this interest, there being four other martyrdom panels extant – including one in Nottingham Castle Museum – and seven standing figures of the saint, who usually balanced a similar flanking figure of St Stephen on the alabaster altarpieces.

The saint is shown stripped of all his clothes except for his underpants; his arms have been secured behind his back. A highly stylised fire burns strongly, which is tended by two men, one with an armful of faggots, the other blowing the fire white-hot with a pair of bellows. In the centre of the panel stands the crowned figure of the Roman Emperor, the edge of his falchion cruelly resting on the body of the saint. On each side of the Emperor stand two torturers wearing hats, both prodding the saint with heated iron pitchforks, as described in *The Golden Legend*[2]. A serene smile is on the face of St Lawrence showing his supreme contempt for the imperial torture.

Details on the panel are beautifully carved, in particular the medieval daggers of the two torturers, the Emperor's falchion, the small costrel hanging from the belt of one of the two men attending the fire and the bellows of the other. Some paint survives, now blackened, on the hats of the torturers and on the two figures at the bottom of the panel, as well as on the saint's underpants.

The panel is set into a wooden framework, which bears a Latin inscription below. Above the panel is a separate alabaster canopy, with some red paint still showing. The usual gothic traceries of the canopy are now missing, but the apertures which were behind them are to be seen.

Alabaster
15th century

Measures: 55.5 cms x 26.5 cms

NOTES

[1] *The Golden Legend,* translated by W G RYAN, Princeton (1993), Vol II, p 63-74.
[2] *The Golden Legend,* translated by W G RYAN, Princeton (1993), Vol II, p 67.

The Annunciation, alabaster, England, 15th century. Musée de Douai, France.

The Virgin who has a halo behind her head on which she wears a fillet, kneels on a tasselled cushion and half turns towards the angel Gabriel[1]. Her hands are raised apart in the attitude of prayer. She wears a gown and a cloak fastened at the front with a brooch. Gabriel kneels on a ledge, his right hand raised in salutation, his left holding a scroll which still bears part of the painted inscription 'Ave Maria gratia plena' (Hail Mary full of grace). The first word of Gabriel's salutation, 'Ave', was seen as a divine pun, reminding the viewer that Mary was the second Eve or Eva. The inscription is twined round a lily plant in an ewer, the lily symbolising both purity and springtime - the Feast of the Annunciation being on 25th March – Lady Day. On Mary's left is a desk, the top of which is covered by a cloth on which lies a book, doubtless opened at Isaiah's prophecy in Latin: 'Virgo Pari et Filium' – (Behold, a virgin shall conceive, and bear a son)[2]. A panel in the V&A Museum still bears this painted inscription[3] which was interpreted as prophesying the conception and birth of Jesus.

Behind the desk are the curtains hanging from the top of a turreted, rather grand, medieval bed.

In the top left of the panel is the half length figure of God the Father his right hand raised in blessing, with an orb in his left. Two small rough patches of alabaster on God the Father's chest and below his left hand, indicate that the usual figure of a dove, representing the Holy Spirit has been broken off. Annunciations with a dove descending from God the Father – often from his mouth – are the most common designs of the 15th century, although occasionally a diminutive Christ Child is shown instead. Up to seventy Annunciation panels with a dove are recorded, only eleven with the small Christ Child. Both designs are present in the V&A Museum. In the Musée de Douai, for example, there is a panel showing the dove, with a wafer in its beak.

Above our panel there is a separate carved canopy in alabaster with four gothic 'windows' – such canopies were usual on the 15th century altarpieces.

Some paint survives, now rather darkened, on the inside of Mary's cloak, on the bottom of the reading desk, on the ground at the bottom of the panel, behind God the Father, and under the canopy which also has lines of gold as if to simulate a vaulted ceiling.

In all some one hundred Annunciation panels survive. The Annunciation was usually the first panel (after a standing saint) in the standard Life of the Virgin altarpieces, such as the Swansea altarpiece in the V&A Museum, which accounts for the high number. In addition of course, the Annunciation was a very suitable subject for an individual panel used for prayer and contemplation.

Alabaster
15th century

Measures: 56 cms x 26 cms

NOTES

[1] LUKE, 1: 26-38
[2] ISAIAH, 7: 14
[2] F CHEETHAM, *English Medieval Alabasters*, Oxford (1984), p 173, cat 100, illus.

29

The Adoration of the Magi, alabaster, England, 15ᵗʰ
century. Archiepiscopal Museum, Köln, Germany.

The Virgin, with a halo behind her head on which she wears a band or fillet, is sitting up on a canopied bed. The canopy is a less ornate version than that in the Annunciation panel in this exhibition. The remarkably agile Christ Child on her lap looks at the first of the Magi, whilst blessing with his right hand. With his other hand he dips into the contents of the chalice-shaped container which the first of the wise men offers.

Although called simply 'wise men from the east' in the Gospels[1], with their number not specified, they traditionally came to be regarded as three kings and were given the names of Caspar (or Gaspar), Balthasar and Melchior[2]. They also came to represent the three continents of the then known world – Europe, Asia and Africa.

The Gospels[3] describe their arrival: 'And when they were come into the house, they saw the young child with Mary his mother, and fell down, and worshipped him: and when they had opened their treasures, they presented unto him gifts; gold, and frankincense, and myrrh.'

The first king, Caspar, holding his crown in his left hand, offers gold, the symbol of kingship. The beardless Balthasar and Melchior, both wearing crowns, offer respectively frankincense to signify the divinity of Christ and myrrh symbolising death. Caspar wears fashionable pointed shoes and a tunic with a low belt, and like Balthasar and Melchior he has a small cape or tippet. The two kings at the back of the panel are pointing upwards to the 'star in the east'[4], situated on the bed canopy.

At the bottom left of the panel sits the figure of Joseph, shown as an old man, with a staff in his left hand and with his head resting on his right.

The manger is also in the foreground, with the two animals traditionally associated with the Nativity, namely the ox and the ass, both looking remarkably alike, who are not in fact mentioned specifically in the Gospel account. However, from the fourth century onwards, these two creatures became an essential part of the Nativity and the Adoration, to justify and fulfil the prophecy of Isaiah[5]. 'The ox knoweth his owner, and the ass his master's crib.' They are also mentioned in *The Golden Legend*[6].

There is some colour on the panel. red in the folds of the cloaks of the Magi, and on the mane of one of the animals. The top of the manger is green and the bottom of the panel is green decorated with the usual daisy pattern. The top of the panel is gilded, with white spots showing where the gesso blobs have come off.

Panels of the Adoration of the Magi are relatively common, for not only were they suitable as individual panels for devotion, but were also almost always included in the standard altarpieces of the Life of the Virgin. Over one hundred are recorded, including nine in the V&A Museum. A typical example, but with the design in reverse and with Mary already wearing a crown, is in the Archiepiscopal Museum in Cologne.

Alabaster
Second half of the 15ᵗʰ century

Measures: 43 cms x 27.5 cms

NOTES

[1] MATTHEW 2:1
[2] *The Golden Legend*, translated by W G RYAN, Princeton
(1993), Vol I, p 79.
[3] MATTHEW 2:11
[4] MATTHEW 2:2
[5] ISAIAH 1:3
[6] *The Golden Legend*, translated by W G RYAN, Princeton
(1993), Vol I, p 38.

The Assumption and Coronation of the Virgin, alabaster, England, 15ᵗʰ century. Musées Royaux d'Art et d'Histoire, Brussels, Belgium.

The Virgin stands bareheaded in a mandorla, hands apart uplifted in prayer, forming the dominant feature of the panel. She wears a close fitting gown, over which is a long tunic. Her shoes protrude below. Her cloak is fastened in an elaborate way by a tasselled cord, the two strands of which are held together with a toggle, and looped over down the front. This is a form of fastening which was fashionable in the 15ᵗʰ century, and is to be seen on both female and male alabaster effigies of the period. For example, on the tomb of Lady Bardolf at Dennington, Suffolk, and on the tomb of Lady Neville at Harewood, Yorkshire[1]. A male weeper on the tomb of Nicholas Fitzherbert who died in 1473 at Norbury, Derbyshire, has a similar fastening[2].

Four angels steady the mandorla, and at the top of the panel two more angels hold a large triple crown surmounted by a cross, over the Virgin's head.

At the bottom of the panel, on the left at the Virgin's feet, kneels the small bearded figure of St Thomas, wearing a gown and cloak which is fastened at the neck by a round brooch. On St Thomas's hands which he holds together in prayer, rests the Virgin's belt, the buckle clearly visible. The Virgin dropped her belt during the Assumption as a tangible demonstration to doubting Thomas of the truth of the Assumption. The *Golden Legend*[3] describes the event: (Mary) 'was assumed into the heavenly bridal chamber, a great multitude of angels keeping her company. Thomas, however, was absent, and when he came back refused to believe. Then suddenly the girdle that had encircled her body fell intact into his hands, and he realised that the Blessed Virgin had really been assumed body and soul.'

The Assumption of the Virgin, body and soul, into heaven, has traditionally been the belief of the Church, even though it was not formally defined as dogma until 1950 by Pope Pius XII. Her Assumption and her Coronation, in this panel by angels, although more commonly by the Trinity, was a symbolic and colourful demonstration of the Church's belief in the appreciation and reward by God of the part played by Mary in the Incarnation and Redemption, by consenting to be the mother of God the Son.

Very little paint survives, although traces of the zigzag pattern on the edge of the mandorla are still visible.

Some one hundred panels of the Assumption are extant, for it was the usual final panel (together with the Coronation) on altarpieces of the Life of the Virgin, such as we may see on the Swansea altarpiece in the V&A Museum, where the Assumption is combined with a Coronation by the Trinity. A panel in the Musées Royaux d'Art et d'Histoire in Brussels unusually shows the Trinity as three separate individuals instead of the dove representing the Holy Spirit.

Alabaster
Second half of the 15ᵗʰ century

Measures: 39 cms x 25 cms

NOTES

[1] A GARDNER, *Alabaster Tombs,* Cambridge (1940), figs 176, 178, 114.
[2] A GARDNER, *Alabaster Tombs,* Cambridge (1940), fig 35.
[3] *The Golden Legend,* translated by W G RYAN, Princeton (1993), Vol II, p 82.

The Agony in the Garden, alabaster, England, 15th century.
Art Museum, Princeton University, USA.

The centre of the panel is dominated by the kneeling figure of Christ, a halo behind his head, his hands together in prayer, from which issues a scroll (broken) bearing the incised words which, in Latin, appear to be the words of Jesus recorded in the Gospels, 'Father, if it be possible, let this cup pass from me'[1]. The cup which symbolised Christ's agony, is represented by a chalice surmounted by the host, reminding the viewer of the Mass and the Eucharist.

Above the chalice appears the hand of God pointing to another scroll with incised words in Latin.

Unable to remain awake while Christ prayed[2], the figures of St Peter identified by his key, St John the Evangelist identified by his clean-shaven face and St James the Great holding a sword with which he was executed[3], are resting.

The Garden of Gethsemane and the Mount of Olives are cleverly represented by the tree with its curious polyhedral foliage and the fence which stretches from the top of the panel and down the side on the right. On 15th century continental woodcuts of the scene, the fence is usually shown, but made of wattle not planks of wood. Outside the fence, foreshadowing the Betrayal, can be observed the heads of three soldiers (one head damaged), one soldier holding a bill. Considering the size of the panel there is a surprising amount of detail included to give us the full flavour of the scene.

There is a little colour on the panel, some gold on the hair of the figures and on the fence at the top. The cross on Christ's halo, painted in gold, denotes divinity[4]. A small amount of red is on the cloak of St Peter, and green is on the ground at the bottom of the panel, on St James's scabbard and on Christ's cloak. The faces of the soldiers – as villains – are coloured black. Unusually, the wording on the two scrolls is incised instead of being simply painted on.

The Agony in the Garden was not usually included in the standard sets of the Passion of Christ altarpieces, and consequently it is not very common. Only seven panels are recorded. There is one in the V&A Museum[5] and a particularly narrow panel in the Art Museum, Princeton University, USA.

Alabaster
15th century

Measures: 39 cms x 27.5 cms

NOTES

[1] MATTHEW 26: 39
[2] MARK 14: 40
[3] ACTS 12:2
[4] E MÂLE, *The Gothic Image*, London (1961), p 2.
[5] F CHEETHAM, *English Medieval Alabasters*, Oxford (1984), p 223, Cat 150, illus.

The Betrayal, alabaster, England, 15th century. Musée des Antiquités, Rouen, France.

The panel represents the dramatic events in the Garden of Gethsemane when Judas, having led the men of the chief priests and Pharisees to Jesus, betrayed him with a kiss[1]. Christ is shown in the centre of the panel facing right, a large halo behind his head, wearing a tunic over a long gown. A soldier who is in the act of drawing his sword (broken) from his scabbard grasps the tunic as if to prevent Christ from leaving.

There are five soldiers in all, wearing helmets and armour. One soldier on the right holds a lantern aloft, while two others rest their hands on their battleaxes. Judas places his left hand on Christ's shoulder, with his face close to him as if to kiss him.

To the left of Christ stands St Peter, tonsured and bearded, holding the handle of his sword which he appears to be replacing in the scabbard, after striking off the ear of the recumbent figure of Malchus, the high priest's servant[2] who lies on the ground, his arm raised in protest. Malchus wearing a tunic with a low belt and holding a staff in his right hand is, like the soldiers, dressed in medieval garb as is usual in medieval art.

There is some colour still on the panel. A little red on the lantern and on the cloaks of St Peter and Judas. The usual green, decorated with daises, is at the bottom of the panel, and there are traces of gold on the upper background.

Being a subject which was usually included as standard in the altarpieces of the Passion of Christ, such as the altarpiece at Nottingham Castle Museum, Betrayal panels are common, there being over one hundred recorded. There are eight (including fragments) in the V&A Museum. The design of the Betrayal panels throughout the 15th century did not change significantly. A panel in the Musée des Antiquités in Rouen is very similar to the one in this exhibition.

Alabaster
15th century

Measures: 41 cms x 27 cms

NOTES

[1] LUKE 22: 47-50
[2] JOHN 18: 10-11

THE FLAGELLATION

Flagellation, alabaster, England, 15th century. Musée de Douai, France.

The embattled top of the panel indicates an early 15th century date. The figure of Christ, naked but for a loin cloth, stands with his arms round a column and bound at the wrists. Around him are four torturers, each with a scourge lifted in the air, with which to strike the defenceless Jesus. The panel represents the episode, mentioned in all the Gospels except Luke, of the scourging ordered by Pilate before the crucifixion. (Part of the actual original column is claimed to be preserved in the church of Santa Prassede in Rome).

The torturers are dressed in medieval gear – normal in medieval art, even though a scene from Roman times is being shown. Notable are the tight tunics and low belts of the two men at the lower part of the panel, and their curious conical hats, which denote they are Jews[1]. The two men in the upper part of the panel wear typical long belted gowns, and one has a coxcomb decoration on his head. There are traces of black colour on their faces. This is a feature which may well derive from a convention of the medieval theatre, enabling the audience to easily identify the villains. The rough faces of the torturers contrast with the finely carved head of Christ.

Apart from the traces of black on the faces, there is a little red colour, especially on the battlements and on the scourges of the torturers. There is also a little gold on the hair and beard of Christ. Much of the typical green ground, decorated with daises, survives.

Seventy four Flagellation panels are recorded, of which five are in the V&A Museum. An almost identical panel[2], with the same Jewish conical hats, is in the Musée de Douai, and is evidently by the same sculptor. On the Douai panel, more black paint survives on the faces of the four torturers, in contrast to the clean unpainted face of Christ.

The Flagellation was included in all the standard altarpieces of the Passion of Christ, such as the one in Nottingham Castle Museum. It is almost certain that the panel in this exhibition was part of such an altarpiece.

Alabaster
Early 15th century

Measures: 42 cms x 26.5 cms

NOTES

[1] E MÂLE, *The Gothic Image*, London (1961), p 3 note 1, p 159.
[2] P NELSON, *Archaeological Journal* LXXV (1918), p 325, pl XIII, 1.

The Crucifixion, alabaster, England, 15ᵗʰ century.
Ashmolean Museum, Oxford.

By the end of the 14ᵗʰ century, the alabastermen started producing altarpieces made up of vertical panels attached to a wooden framework, and usually illustrating either the Passion of Christ or the Life of the Virgin. The carving in this exhibition would almost certainly have been the central panel of such an altarpiece, although unlike the later altarpieces, the central panel was not taller than the others in the set. The embattled top is a characteristic of many of the early 15ᵗʰ century panels.

Christ is shown on the cross, more in the tradition of the Romanesque Christ Triumphant, rather than the piteously suffering Christ of the late Middle Ages. He looks down at his mother who is being supported in her grief by Mary Magdalene and Mary Cleophas.

On the right of the panel stands the bearded figure of the centurion wearing a large red coloured hat, a belted tunic and cloak. With his right hand he points towards Christ. In a crucifixion panel in the V&A Museum[1], there is a scroll issuing from the hand of the centurion bearing the painted inscription, 'Veri filius dei' (Truly the Son of God). On many alabaster Crucifixions, St John the Evangelist is shown, usually carrying a palm, but he is not represented on our panel. There are however, two male beardless figures behind the centurion, although neither appears to be St John.

The Crucifixion scene would have been very familiar to medieval people, for the rood screen at the east end of the nave was an essential element in the internal furnishings of every church before the Reformation. The rood screen showed the two figures of the Virgin and St John beneath the figure of Christ on the cross.

There is some red colour surviving on the inside of the cloak and on the hat of the centurion. Much gold leaf is also on the hair of the figures and on the background where the bare dots were once gold painted blobs of gesso. The faces of the figures have been painted a flesh colour.

As one would expect, many Crucifixions survive, in fact no less than one hundred and twenty seven are recorded, although a Crucifixion panel was not invariably present on the Passion of Christ altarpieces. Sometimes a panel of the Trinity, which of course includes the figure of Christ on the cross, occupies the central position, as for example on the altarpiece in Nottingham Castle Museum.

The later 15ᵗʰ century and early 16ᵗʰ century panels were usually of a more crowded design, which included the crucifixion of the two thieves. The figure of Longinus with his spear with which he pierced Christ's side also appears together with the centurion. Longinus is now differentiated from the centurion, who earlier was identified as Longinus himself[2]. Examples are in the Ashmolean Museum, Oxford, and the V&A Museum[3].

Alabaster
C 1400

Measures: 45 cms x 26 cms

NOTES

[1] F CHEETHAM, *English Medieval Alabasters,* Oxford
(1984), p 249, cat 176, illus.
[2] *The Golden Legend,* translated by W G RYAN, Princeton
(1993), Vol I, p 184.
[3] F CHEETHAM, *English Medieval Alabasters,* Oxford
(1984), pp 252-258, illus.

41

The Entombment of Our Lord, alabaster, England, 15th century. Bayrisches National Museum, Munich, Germany.

Christ is shown being lowered into the tomb. A shroud covers the lower part of his body and on his head he wears a twisted cord or torse representing the crown of thorns. Joseph of Arimathea who wears a mitre-shaped hat (top missing), tippet and gown, with a purse hanging from his belt, holds the body of Christ round the hips. Nicodemus, wearing a bag-crowned hat and tippet over his gown, steadies the head and shoulder of Christ. According to the gospel accounts, Christ was buried in Joseph of Arimathea's own tomb, hewn in stone[1]. The sepulchre is however shown here as a typical medieval tomb. Nicodemus brought a mixture of myrrh and aloes and they then wound the body of Jesus in linen cloths with the spices[2].

The Virgin Mary, a halo behind her head and hands clasped together in an attitude of despair and grief, stands in the centre of the panel, behind the tomb. Behind her are two bare-headed women, Mary Cleophas and Mary Salome. All three women have almost identical brooches fastening the front of their cloaks.

In the top right corner of the panel is a figure, whose head has been damaged, but is clearly identified by the palm he is holding as St John the Evangelist. Forming the background to these figures is the top of the cross.

Mary Magdalene is kneeling in front of the tomb on the left of the panel, and wipes the ointment from Christ's left hand with her long hair. Her emblem, the alabaster box of very precious ointment[3], stands on a ledge.

Very little paint survives, mainly darkened green at the bottom of the panel and on the palm of St John the Evangelist.

The Entombment was a popular subject mainly because it was one of the standard scenes in the Passion of Christ altarpieces, such as may be seen in Nottingham Castle Museum.

Doubtless our panel was from such an altarpiece originally. One hundred panels are recorded, including seven in the V&A Museum. Of the many such panels surviving a typical example is the Bayrisches National Museum, Munich.

Alabaster
15th century

Measures: 41 cms x 25 cms

NOTES

[1] LUKE 23: 50-53
[2] JOHN 19: 39-40
[3] MARK 14: 3-8

43

The Resurrection, alabaster, England, 15ᵗʰ century. Ferens Art Gallery, Hull.

Christ wearing the torse on his head, a loincloth, and the shroud over his shoulders, raises his right hand in blessing and in his left, he holds the cross-staff of the Resurrection. He steps from the tomb onto the body of a sleeping moustachioed soldier, who wears a helmet, a tippet of mail over his shoulders, a low-belted jupon, gauntlets and armour. From his belt hangs a dagger and with his right hand he grasps the top of the shaft of a large battleaxe.

The placing of one of Christ's feet actually onto a sleeping soldier as he steps from the tomb is a common feature in English alabaster Resurrections, but this is a detail which is rare in continental art. Dr Hildburgh, who generously presented most of the alabaster carvings in the collection of the V&A Museum, has suggested that the influence of the medieval mystery plays was responsible for this feature as well as for the conventional medieval tomb, instead of the original cave-like sepulchre described in the Gospels.

Hildburgh[1] has pointed out that the Saviour's foot rests on the soldier so as to give the actor a useful stepping block as he emerged from the tomb, and the cross-staff would have rendered valuable service to an actor having to step in a dignified way out of a deep chest. The tomb chest itself, enabled the actor to hide unseen until the dramatic moment of the Resurrection itself. All this is simply hypothesis, but an ingenious one and possibly having a factual basis.

Three other soldiers, clad in armour, are shown. The one on the left of the panel, sitting on a projection on the outside of the tomb looks up in surprise and is about to draw his sword from its sheath. The soldier holding a battleaxe on the right, sitting on a projection which also conveniently sticks out from the side of the tomb, looks at the figure of Christ. The third soldier with a spear, on the upper right of the panel, looks away from the scene, his head resting on his hand, apparently asleep.

Above in the top corners of the panel, two angels are swinging censers.

Just a little colour survives. Red on one of the angel's wings, and green decorated with the characteristic daisy pattern made up of five white dots surrounding a red dot.

The Resurrection scene was present in all the altarpieces of the Passion of Christ, and it was, of course, also a suitable subject for an individual panel to be used for devotional purposes.

No less than one hundred and forty four panels are recorded, including ten in the V&A Museum. A particularly attractive Resurrection panel is in the Ferens Art Gallery, Hull. It was purchased with help from the National Art Collections Fund and the National Association of Decorative & Fine Arts Societies, from Daniel Katz Ltd in 1999.

Alabaster
15ᵗʰ century

Measures: 39 cms x 24.5 cms

NOTES

[1] W L HILDBURGH, *Archaeologia* XCIII (1949), pp 90-93.

The Trinity, alabaster, England, 15th century. Musée des Beaux Arts, Ghent, Belgium.

Alabaster
15th century

Measures: 49.5 cms x 27 cms

NOTES

[1] G ZARNECKI, *Studies in Romanesque Sculpture* (1979), pls 13a and b.
[2] LUKE 16: 22
[3] E MÂLE, *The Gothic Image,* London (1961), p 384.

This elegant carving shows the Trinity surrounded by angels. God the Father is crowned and seated on a throne holding a napkin between his wrists containing three diminutive heads. In the lower part of the panel is God the Son on the cross with four angels holding chalices to catch the precious blood issuing from his wounds.

God the Holy Spirit does not at first sight appear to be represented. But there is a dowel hole above the head of Christ to which a small carved dove was originally attached. It was a curious technique of the alabastermen to carve the dove separately and plug it into a hole near the top of the cross. There are a number of Trinity panels in the V&A Museum which have the same arrangement, although sometimes the dove was carved as an integral part of the panel, as we can also see in the V&A Museum. More rarely there is neither dowel hole nor dove. In such a case the dove may have been painted onto the alabaster, or curiously even missed out altogether.

To try to represent visually the creator of the universe, is of course, an impossible challenge and which early Christian artists were reluctant to attempt. Gradually however, the concept of representing God as a venerable old man developed – doubtless influenced by the concept of the Christian God as father, an idea implicit in the Lord's Prayer.

The three diminutive heads represent the souls of the blessed taken to the bosom of God the Father. These 15th century souls in a napkin have been inspired by the earlier Romanesque and thirteenth century carvings of the souls of the blessed in the bosom of Abraham such as we find at Lincoln Cathedral, and on the central doorway of the Abbey of St Denis[1], and illustrating the text about the beggar Lazarus – 'And it came to pass that the beggar died and was carried by angels into Abraham's bosom'[2].

Much of the original medieval paint survives. In particular the red of the angels' wings and the characteristic green decorated with a daisy pattern at the bottom of the panel and on the cross itself. Gold leaf has been applied to the background at the top of the panel – again a characteristic of many 15th century alabaster panels. The white spots were originally blobs of decorative gesso which have fallen off. The two angels near the head of God the Father were originally swinging censers which are now missing.

Trinities are relatively common, over one hundred are recorded for they often formed the central panel of an altarpiece, and the subject was also attractive for private devotions – alabaster images were certainly present in wealthy private houses as well as in churches. The depiction of angels catching the blood of Christ in chalices on the panel, would remind the viewer of the real bodily presence of Christ in the Mass. God holding the souls was a welcome illustration of God's mercy and indeed Emile Mâle describing the earlier thirteenth century carving of Abraham holding the souls of the blessed at Reims Cathedral, has written[3] 'Never was reverence for the soul of man or faith in immortality better expressed...'. However Trinities featuring the souls of the blessed are much fewer in number, only nineteen are recorded. A typical image of the Trinity – freestanding, not a panel – showing the carved dove, but lacking the souls of the blessed is in the Musée des Beaux Arts, Ghent, Belgium.

THE TENTH SIGN OF THE LAST JUDGEMENT

The Tenth Sign of the Last Judgement, alabaster, England, 15th century. British Museum, London.

The Golden Legend describes the Fifteen Signs, said originally to derive from the Annals of the Hebrews by Saint Jerome, which will precede the Last Judgement. The present panel appears to be the Tenth Sign[1] which is described as '... men will come out of the caves and go about as if demented, unable to speak to each other.' – quite a difficult concept to describe in sculpture. This panel may be compared with one in the British Museum, also of the Tenth Sign, which has a canopy carved as an integral part of the panel.

Three male figures wearing long pointed shoes and long tunics with baggy sleeves, dominate the design of the panel. Two of the men wear very low belts. The central figure has a tall floppy hat and a tippet or short cape. The figure on the right wears a type of turban, while the man kneeling on the left is bare headed, his hands together, apparently in prayer. The clothing of the men was fashionable in the mid 15th century. The trees with their curious bulbous foliage and the green painted uneven surface decorated with daisies, indicate a scene which is out of doors. Above the trees on the right is an angel, a scroll issuing from his right hand, the painted inscription now missing.

The panel in the British Museum, while containing more individuals has a number of features which are similar to details in our panel, especially the low-belted tunics, the men's headgear and the angel holding a scroll. In both panels the figures do not appear to be communicating with each other, each is in his own 'little world' and hence illustrate the Tenth Sign.

Panels of Signs of the Last Judgement are not common, only ten are recorded. A panel of the Fifteenth Sign, the resurrection of the dead, in the Musée Robin, Libourne, appears to be from the same altarpiece, now dismembered, as two other panels in the same museum, one of St Peter receiving the Souls of the Blessed and the other of the Damned led into Hell[2]. From these surviving panels we may deduce that there were Last Judgement altarpieces which included some of the Signs, as well as a dramatic illustration of what happened to the good and the bad.

Alabaster
Mid 15th century

Measures: 38 cms x 24 cms

NOTES

[1] *The Golden Legend*, translated by W G RYAN, Princeton (1993), p 8.
[2] J GARDELLES, '*Sculpture Médiévale de Bordeaux et du Bordelais*', Musée d'Aquitaine (1976), p 207, nos 195-197, illus.

Head of St John the Baptist, alabaster, England, 15ᵗʰ century. Aberdeen Art Gallery, Scotland.

Alabaster
Late 15ᵗʰ century
On Loan from Norfolk Museum and Archaeology Service

Measures: 30.4 cms x 15 cms

NOTES

[1] F CHEETHAM, *English Medieval Alabasters*, Oxford (1984), p 322, cat 246, illus.
[1] F CHEETHAM, *English Medieval Alabasters*, Oxford (1984), p 324, cat 248, illus.
[3] *Bury St Edmunds' Wills and Inventories* (1850), p 115.
[4] JOHN I: 29
[5] S FOISTER, *Burlington Magazine*, CXXIII (May 1981), pp 273-82.
[6] F CHEETHAM, *English Medieval Alabasters*, Oxford (1984), p 317.

The severed head of St John the Baptist on a dish takes the central position on this finely carved panel. His hair falls in points onto his forehead and then sweeps down the sides of the Head ending in a forked beard. Above, two angels hold a small naked child kneeling in a mandorla, symbolising the soul of the Baptist being taken up into heaven.

We may be sure that the head is indeed of St John the Baptist, for a number of panels still bear a painted inscription in Latin on the dish stating this. There are for example two panels in the V & A Museum with such an inscription, one bearing the words 'Caput sci ihohanis baptiste I disco'[1], the other with '(C) aput sci Johis Baptiste.'[2].

On the left of the panel is St Peter holding a key (broken) and a book, and on the right a bishop with mitre, book and cross-staff. The bishop is almost certainly that most popular of medieval canonised English bishops, namely St Thomas Becket. Indeed a will dated 1552 of Agas Herte of Bury St Edmunds describes such a panel '... Seynt Johis hede of alabast wt Seynt Pet and Seynt Thomas and the fygur of Cryst.'[3].

Much of the original paint survives. Gold on the hair of the angels and of the saints and on the mandorla; red on the angels' wings and on the inside of the saints' cloaks; dark brown on the tomb and on the hair of Christ and green on the ground.

Below the Head, flanked by the two standing saints is the figure of Christ the Man of Sorrows, or to use the medieval term, the Jesus Pity. He wears the twisted wreath or torse to represent the crown of thorns and a loincloth. He stands in the tomb showing his wounds.

The iconography of the panels of the Head of St John the Baptist is somewhat complex. The Agnus Dei, or Lamb of God emblem showing a lamb, usually holding a cross, is on many of the panels instead of the Jesus Pity. The Agnus Dei is of course the emblem of St John the Baptist and the symbol of Christ himself. It reminds the viewer of the words of St John recorded in the Gospels[4] and spoken by the priest during the Mass as he holds up the consecrated Host for the congregation to see: 'Ecce Agnus Dei, ecce qui tollis peccata mundi', (Behold the Lamb of God. Behold Him who takes away the sins of the world). The Jesus Pity was of course a more direct image of Christ than the Agnus Dei and since the tomb in which Christ stands reminded the viewer of the altar, was even more powerful, although the St John the Baptist connection was less obvious.

Unlike many of the alabaster panels, those of the Head of St John the Baptist were not designed to fit into an altarpiece but were intended for individual private devotions. Surviving wills indicate that they were popular in homes, for those who could afford them, and certainly some were kept in wooden cupboards or housings, the two doors being opened when the carving was to be contemplated. Sometimes instead of a housing, contemporary inventories[5] refer to 'a Saynt Johns cloth' which could be used to veil the Head when it was not to be viewed.

The Heads were certainly a speciality of the Nottingham carvers. There are a number of references to them in the Records of the Borough of Nottingham[6]. For example, in October 1491, an image maker named Nicholas Hill brought an action against his salesman, William Bott, for the money owing on no less than fifty eight Heads. Many such panels survive. Some ninety seven are recorded, including fourteen in the V & A Museum.

A panel with the Agnus Dei represented is in the City Art Gallery, Aberdeen.

Published by Daniel Katz Ltd. on the occasion of the exhibition

THE ALABASTER MEN
SACRED IMAGES OF MEDIEVAL ENGLAND
30th October to 23rd November 2001

Daniel Katz Ltd.
59 Jermyn Street
London SW1Y 6LX
Telephone 44 (0) 20 7493 0688
Facsimile 44 (0) 20 7499 7493
info@katz.co.uk

ISBN 88-7336-007-6
©, Copyright 2001: Daniel Katz Ltd. and Gli Ori, Italy

Catalogue photography: GERRY CLIST

The Daniel Katz Gallery would like to thank the Norfolk Museum and Archaeology Service
and those private collectors who generously loaned to this exhibition.

Realised by:

Catalogue design: PICCIA G. NERI

Scanning and repro: Screenservice, Comeana, Italy

Printed in Italy at Bandecchi & Vivaldi, Pontedera, Italy